# Learning to COOK

Written by
*Tapasi De*

Illustrated by
*Suman S. Roy*

Mum cooks for us everyday. One day I thought that I would cook something for her.

I began looking through cook books and asked my friends.

I thought hard to find ou
which food would make
mum the most happy.

One day my class
teacher Ms Lily visited
me as I
was sick.

When we were alone,
I asked Ms Lily what I
could cook for mum.

Ms Lily said that I could make sailboat sandwiches for mum.

She said that I would need crescent dinner rolls, tuna salad, cheddar cheese and toothpicks.

I was very happy as Ms Lily told me that I would not need fire to make these sandwiches.

Next day, I counted my pocket money and went shopping in the nearby market.

I went to the market while returning from school so that no one would know about it.

I bought crescent dinner rolls, tuna salad, cheddar cheese and toothpicks.

At first I thought that I would keep this a secret. But I had to tell dad as he would help me.

I asked dad what would
be the right time to do
the cooking. I wanted
to surprise
mum.

Dad said that Saturday
night would be ideal as
mum and dad had to go
to a party. I liked his
idea.

Finally, Saturday came.
I was very excited but
tried not to show it.

The moment dad and mum left, I took out all the items. Then, I placed them on the kitchen table.

Dad had already sliced
the tops off the rolls
and scooped them  out.

I filled the rolls with
the tuna salad.

And then, I closed the mouth of the rolls so that the filling would not come out.

Now that my rolls were ready, I sliced the cheese into rectangles.

Then I cut the rectangles to make triangles. I put a toothpick into each triangle to make the little sails.

Now that my sails were made, I pierced them into the rolls which looked like tiny boats.

Finally, the sandwiches were made. My little brother and my nanny said they looked delicious!

I was happy but I hoped
even mum would like it.

It was very late
when dad and mum
came back.

Next morning, I got up early and served the sandwiches nicely on a plate.

# When mum saw them, she was surprised.

Mum asked who had
made the sandwiches.
When she came to
know that it was me,
she was very happy.

I came running to her and she hugged me. Meanwhile, dad also came.

My parents were both very happy. They said that I had truly grown up!

# Let's spell new words

| | |
|---|---|
| thought | filling |
| visited | nanny |
| sailboat | delicious |
| toothpicks | cheese |
| shopping | secret |
| crescent | market |
| dinner rolls | returning |
| excited | teacher |
| mashed | |
| scooped | |
| rectangles | |